MANGA SAMPLER
2017

Introduction

VIZ Media has an excellent lineup of new manga series for 2017. Within the pages of this sampler, you'll find sequels to some of the world's most iconic manga, as well as new series in genres from fantasy romance and high school drama to action-packed historical fiction. We hope you enjoy this sampler of some of our—and we hope your—favorite new series.

TABLE OF CONTENTS

Dragon Ball Super

Story by Akira Toriyama, Art by Toyotarou

Ever since Goku became Earth's greatest hero and gathered the seven Dragon Balls to defeat the evil Boo, his life on Earth has grown a little dull. But new threats loom overhead, and Goku and his friends will have to defend the planet once again in this continuation of Akira Toriyama's best-selling series *Dragon Ball*!

...SUPER SAIYAN BLUE?

HOW ABOUT...

BLUE ...?

...

YOU MUST DO AS I SAY IN MY TRAINING SESSIONS.

I TOLD YOU BOTH THAT YOU'RE NOT ALLOWED TO TRANSFORM DURING THIS FIGHT!

AREN'T YOU BEING A LITTLE TOO COCKY...

...JUST BECAUSE YOU DEFEATED GOLDEN FREEZA?

TMP

FSHT

THANKS TO THAT, THEY WERE ABLE TO DEFEAT THE RESURRECTED FREEZA ...

AFTER MEETING WITH BEERUS, GOKU AND VEGETA WENT TO WHIS FOR TRAINING. THEIR STRENGTH EVOLVED INTO A POWER THAT SURPASSED EVEN THE GOD FORM-- SUPER SAIYAN BLUE!

THERE WAS AN INCIDENT RECENTLY WHERE FREEZA, THE EMPEROR OF TERROR WHO ONCE THREATENED TO DESTROY THE UNIVERSE, WAS RESURRECTED AND WENT TO ATTACK THE EARTH..

GEEZ ...

RMBL RMBL

LET'S SAY... HOW ABOUT A FIGHT BETWEEN GROUPS OF FIVE?

NO, IT HAS TO BE BATTLES FOUGHT BY CHOSEN WARRIORS FROM OUR UNIVERSES.

I'M TALKING ABOUT A HAND-TO-HAND FIGHT. IF I WIN, WE SWITCH UNIVERSES.

HA HA HA! WHAT'S THIS? BE-TWEEN YOU AND ME?

YEEEEEES!!

WE'LL HOLD A GODS OF DESTRUCTION INVITATIONAL FIGHTING TOURNAMENT!

ONE-ON-ONE BATTLES. AND WHOEVER WIPES OUT THE OTHER TEAM FIRST WINS.

The Water Dragon's Bride

Story and Art by Rei Toma

In the blink of an eye, a modern-day girl named Asahi is whisked away from her warm and happy home and stranded in a strange and mysterious world where she is to be sacrificed to a water dragon god!

YOU...
ARE...

PFFT...

AH HA HA!

THAT WAS A JOKE, RIGHT?

WHICH PART?

AND YOU KNOW WHAT? DAD WAS DOING IT THE WHOLE TIME!

ALL RIGHT, I'LL TELL YOU! I BELIEVED IN HIM UNTIL LAST YEAR!

I GET IT! YOU'RE THE KIND OF KID WHO STILL BELIEVES IN SANTA!

SANTA...?
?

?

PWING

I'D
THOUGHT...

YOU
CAN'T...
DO
THIS...

YES...

...MOTHER.

The Legend of Zelda™: Twilight Princess

Story and Art by Akira Himekawa

Once upon a time, wizards tried to conquer the Sacred Realm of Hyrule. The Spirits of Light sealed the wizards' power within the Shadow Crystal and banished them to the Twilight Realm beyond the Mirror of Twilight. Now, an evil menace is trying to find Midna, Princess of the Twilight Realm, and the fragments of the Shadow Crystal to gain the power to rule over both the Twilight Realm and the World of Light.

TALO'S A HANDFUL, BUT HE'S CUTE.

AND COLIN, MALO AND BETH...

I HOPE WE CAN ALL GO FISHING TOGETHER ON YOUR NEXT DAY OFF.

THEY'RE ALL CUTE.

...ME TOO. YEAH...

AWOOO

IT'S A WOLF HOWLING.

IN FARON WOODS?

SHIVER

WHAT IS THAT SOUND?

AWOOOO

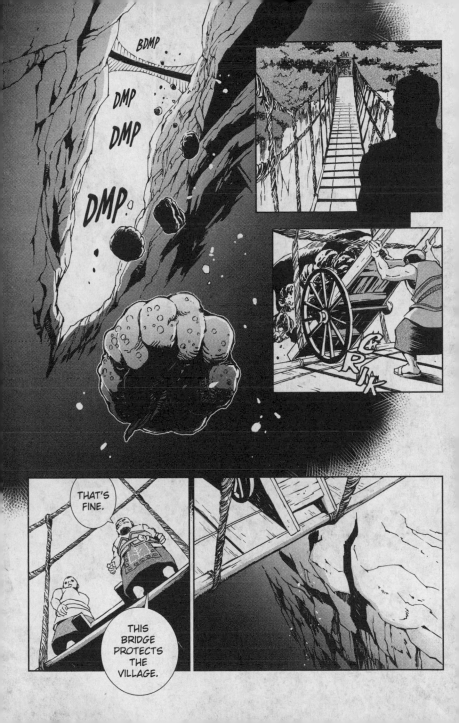

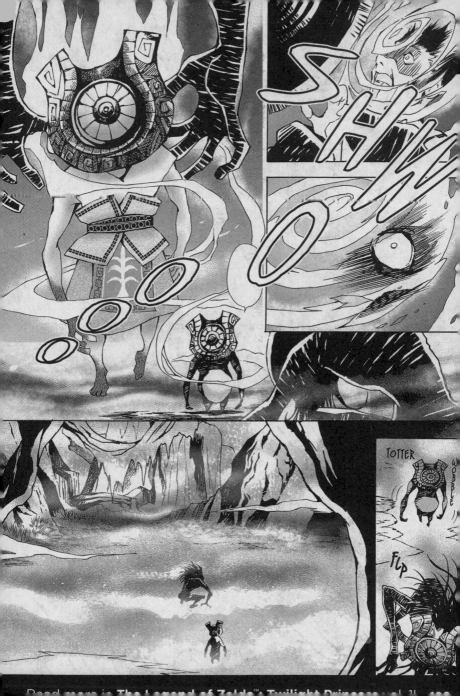

SHHHH

TOTTER
WOBBLE

FLIP

Boruto: Naruto Next Generations

Creator/Supervisor Masashi Kishimoto
Script by Ukyo Kodachi, Art by Mikio Ikemoto

Naruto was a young shinobi with an incorrigible knack for mischief. He achieved his dream to become the greatest ninja in his village, and now his face sits atop the Hokage monument. But this is not his story... A new generation of ninja are ready to take the stage, led by Naruto's own son, Boruto!

YUP.

I'M A NINJA.

...I COULDN'T CARE LESS ABOUT BEING A NINJA.

BUT BACK THEN...

...IS THE TOP NINJA OF THE VILLAGE.

THE HOKAGE...

BUT THIS ISN'T A TALE...

...ABOUT A BOY WHO AIMS TO BECOME HOKAGE.

THAT WAS MY DAD'S STORY.

...NONE OTHER..

THIS IS...

HOW-
EVER...

...THAN
MY
STORY.

...SINCE
I'M THE
HOKAGE'S
SON...

...I CAN'T
HELP THAT
MY DAD
ENDS UP
BEING
INVOLVED IN
MY STORY.

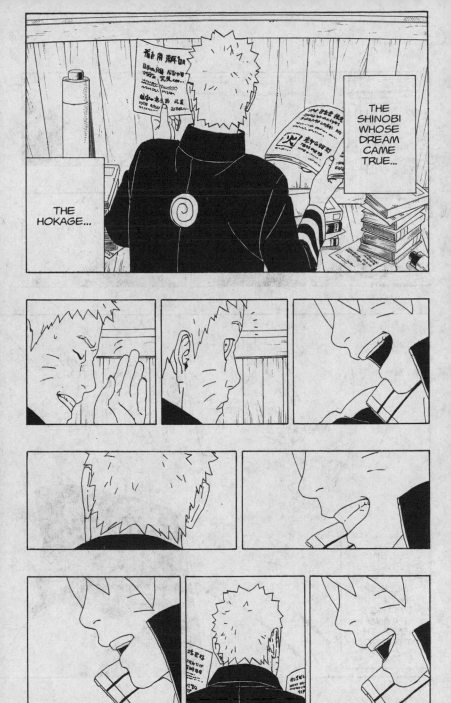

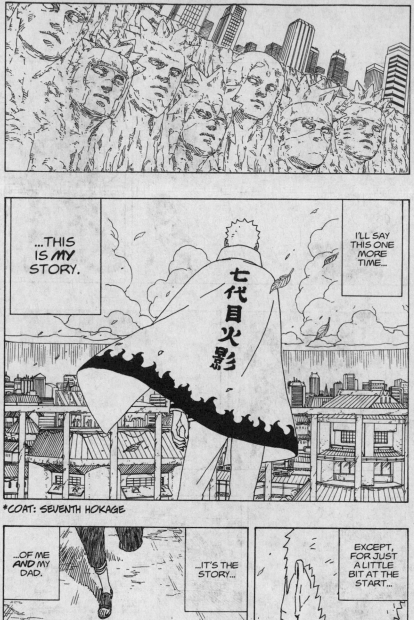

...THIS IS *MY* STORY.

I'LL SAY THIS ONE MORE TIME...

*COAT: SEVENTH HOKAGE

...OF ME *AND* MY DAD.

...IT'S THE STORY...

EXCEPT, FOR JUST A LITTLE BIT AT THE START...

SNAG

SWISH

FWP

SHADOW PARALYSIS JUTSU!

VWOOSH

RAWR... •••

FREEZE

EARLIER, WASN'T THAT...

MASTER KONO-HAMARU?

...A NARA CLAN SECRET JUTSU?

THANK YE SO MUCH.

THE RECOVERY CORPS WILL TAKE CARE OF THE REST.

IS THAT THE NEW NINJA TOOL I HEARD ABOUT?

WHOA, COOL!

OH YEAH, YOU SEE...

NEWS SURE REACHES YOU FAST, MITSUKI!

BEFORE, IT WAS MASTER SHIKAMARU'S SHADOW PARALYSIS JUTSU.

YOU CAN SEAL *ANY* NINJUTSU INSIDE THIS THING.

THAT JUTSU FROM EARLIER IS CONTAINED WITHIN IT?

IT'S SUCH A TINY SCROLL.

...SCIENTIFIC NINJA TOOL CORPS. COLLECTING DATA ON IT WAS ALSO PART OF TODAY'S MISSION.

IT'S A PROTOTYPE FROM THE...

*TEXT: WIND

...I MANAGED THREE SHADOW DOPPEL-GANGERS RIGHT OFF THE BAT...

BUT EVEN WITHOUT ANY TRAINING...

TO TRAIN AS A TRIO AND WORK IN TANDEM...

FOR A SHINOBI, WHAT'S IMPORTANT IS TEAMWORK AND GUTS.

WHAT EXACTLY HAVE YOU BEEN TEACHING HIM?!

SIR?

KONOHA-MARU!!

...AND RECENTLY, EVEN WATER STYLE!

PLUS WIND STYLE, LIGHTNING STYLE...

STOP!!

BAM!

FOR A SHINOBI, WHAT'S IM—

...

LEAVE MASTER KONOHAMARU OUT OF THIS!!

IF YOU FORGET MY LITTLE SISTER'S BIRTHDAY...

TODAY'S AN IMPORTANT DAY *FOR A DAD!*

YOU KNOW WHY, RIGHT?!

...I'LL *NEVER* FORGIVE YOU! GOT THAT?!

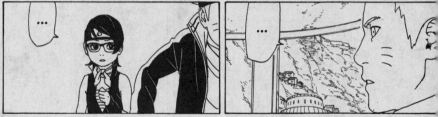

...

...

AH, KATASUKE.

EXCUSE ME...

KLAK

KNOCK KNOCK KNOCK

!

...HERE ARE THE APPLICATION FORMS...

...FOR THE UPCOMING CHUNIN EXAM!

AND SO...

...WE'RE STILL ROOKIES. I DUNNO...

BUT...

WHAT A BOTHER..

WE'RE NOT GOOD ENOUGH YET.

YEAH, MASTER MOEGI.

MUNCH MUNCH

WE'RE GOOD ENOUGH TO ENTER?!

YUP! YOU BETTER GIVE IT YOUR BEST!

!

"THIS NEXUS OF CHURRO TASTING," RIGHT?

YEAH, YEAH.

THIS NEXT CHUNIN TEST...

HEY, ARE YOU LISTENING, CHUBS?!

GLOOO...M

...!!

...ROCK THE TEST, EH, INOJIN?

L-LET'S...

Y-YEAH, TOTALLY, HA HA...

...

WHAT IS IT?

WE'LL FILL THESE OUT LATER!

WELL THEN, SEE YA, MASTER!

OH, RIGHT. WE BETTER GET GOIN'.

HEY, AREN'T WE MEETING UP WITH BORUTO?

...SO COULD WE AT LEAST TALK ABOUT THIS?

WE'RE SUPPOSED TO BE A TEAM...

HEY.

ALL OF US HAVE TO SIGN UP...

...

...TO SHOW LORD SEVENTH HOW AMAZING...

LET'S USE THIS EXAM...

HEY, BORUTO!

...THE THREE OF US ARE!

...

ESPECIALLY YOUR FATHER

I'M SURE EVERYONE'S LOOKING FORWARD TO SEEING YOUR CAPABILITIES.

HE'S SO SIMPLE.

WHEE! ♪

...

YOU WANT ME TO TAKE IT, RIGHT? FINE!

OKAY, ALREADY!

I'VE HEARD DAD SAY THAT...

...MASTER SASUKE IS THE *OTHER* HOKAGE!

WELL THEN, WHAT ABOUT YOURS?

...YOUR DAD'S REALLY AMAZING.

CAN'T YOU BE MORE UNDER-STANDING?

LOOK...

...YOU'VE PROBABLY BEEN THROUGH A LOT, BUT...

WHAT?

...

BUT *MY* PARENT HAS ALSO SAID THAT MASTER SASUKE IS THE ONLY SHINOBI WHO IS LORD HOKAGE'S EQUAL...

...IN FIGHTING ABILITY.

I-I'M SURE HE WAS BEING MODEST.

...HOW FUN IT'S SUPPOSED TO BE TO SPEND TIME AS A FAMILY, RIGHT?!

WHICH MEANS HE GREW UP NOT KNOWIN'...

THEY SAY GRANDPA WAS A HOKAGE TOO, BUT...

...DIDN'T YOU TELL ME...

...THAT WHEN DAD WAS A KID, GRANDPA WASN'T ALIVE ANYMORE?!

I'D RATHER JUST NOT HAVE A PARENT THAN HAVE ONE WHO IS HOKA--

YOU **HAVE** A FATHER WHO'S ALIVE!

...THINGS ARE DIFFERENT FOR YOU THAN THEY WERE FOR HIM!

SURE...

...IT'S SAD THAT YOUR FATHER ISN'T HERE ON IMPORTANT DAYS, BUT...

*CAKE: HAPPY BIRTHDAY

YOU'RE NARUTO'S SON, HUH?

WHAT'S YOUR NAME?

WHOA, S-SORRY!

I THOUGHT YOU WERE MY DAD!

TMP

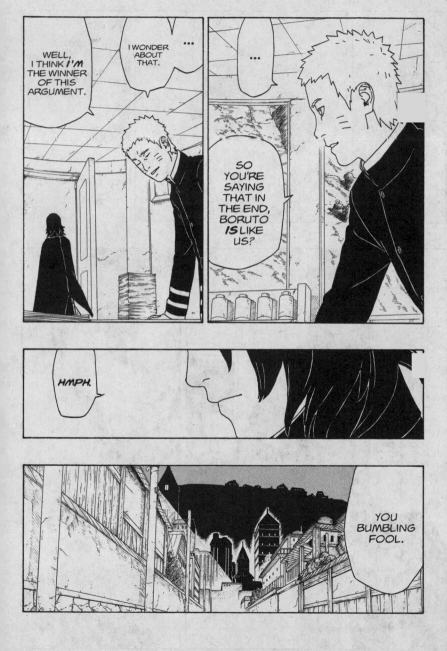

SWSH

HE
VANISH-
ED!

!!

SHF

Anonymous Noise

Story and Art by Ryoko Fukuyama

Nino Arisugawa, a girl who loves to sing, experiences her first heart-wrenching goodbye when her beloved childhood friend, Momo, moves away. And after Nino befriends Yuzu, a music composer, she experiences another sad parting! Both boys promised Nino that they would find her one day through her singing, so she holds on to that hope and continues to reach out with her voice. Now in high school, Nino serendipitously reunites with Yuzu, but she yearns to see Momo again...

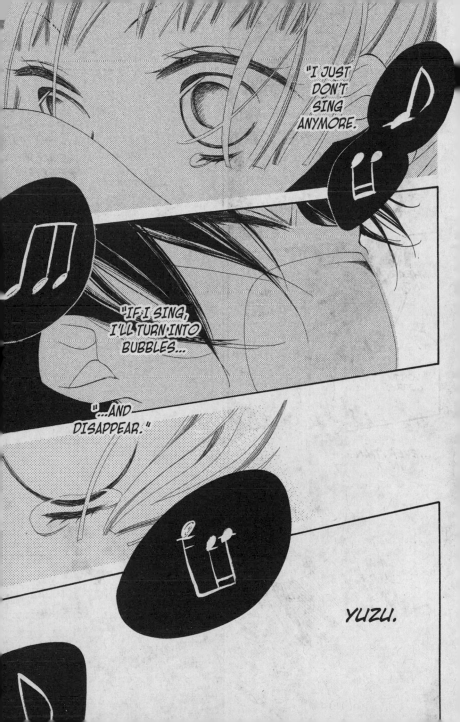

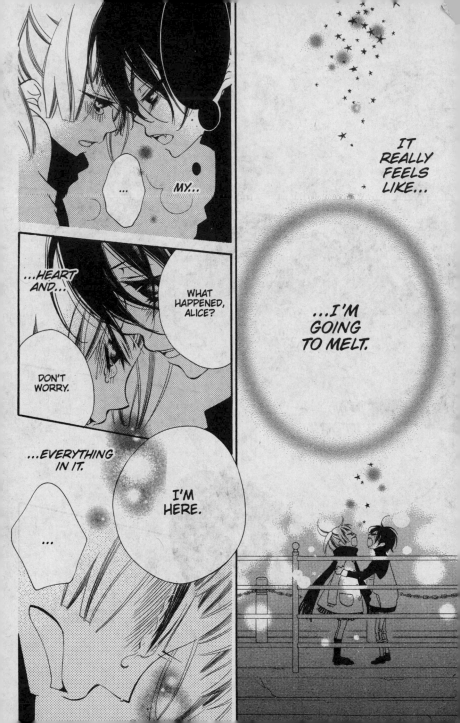

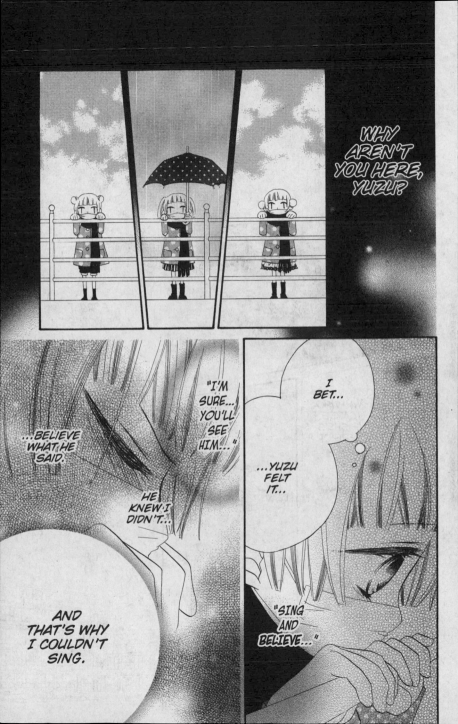

"BECAUSE I WILL NEVER, EVER...

I WANT TO SEE YOU.

YUZU...

"...FORGET YOUR VOICE."

HEY, BALDY.

WH-WHO CARES IF SHE'S HERE OR NOT.

YOU KNOW, LATELY...

...ARISUGAWA'S BEEN COMING IN LATE AND LEAVING EARLY A LOT.

...

YEEAAGH!

I said I'm not bald!

YOU THINK IT'S OUR FAULT?

SOMEHOW, SOMEWAY.

BONNG

BIING

...IT WON'T BE LONG...

...BEFORE WE MEET AGAIN.

Vampire Knight: Memories

Story and Art by Matsuri Hino

After a fierce battle between humans and vampires, a temporary peace was established, but Kaname continued to sleep within a coffin of ice. Yuki gave Kaname her heart to revive him as a human being.

These are the stories of what happened during those 1000 years of Kaname's slumber and at the start of his human life.

...BECAUSE MY FATHER HAD DECIDED I WOULD.

I'M SAYORI WAKABA. I STARTED MIDDLE SCHOOL AT CROSS ACADEMY...

MY FATHER, A GOVERNMENT OFFICIAL, HAD A HABIT OF TREATING PEOPLE LIKE PAWNS.

I NEVER LIKED THAT ABOUT HIM.

THE CYNICISM I ACQUIRED AT AN EARLY AGE WAS DUE TO THAT.

I WAS TOLD MY ROOMMATE AT SCHOOL WOULD BE THE HEAD-MASTER'S DAUGHTER.

HER NAME WAS YUKI CROSS.

SHE WAS A MODEST GIRL WHO LAUGHED A LOT.

W—WHAT?

I THOUGHT...

IT'S PROBABLY BECAUSE MY FATHER THINKS OUR BEING FRIENDS WILL BE A GOOD THING—

SAYORI!

MY FATHER TOLD ME TO BECOME FRIENDS WITH YOU.

I WANT TO BE FAIR TO YOU, SO I'LL TELL YOU STRAIGHT OUT...

DON'T WORRY. YOUR NEW FRIEND WON'T SUDDENLY TRANSFER TO A DIFFERENT SCHOOL THIS TIME.

THIS WAS THE FIRST TIME I SAW THE THREE OF THEM TOGETHER.

YUKI.

KANAME-SAMA!

THIS KANAME-SAMA INSINUATED THAT HE WAS THE REASON BEHIND HER NOT HAVING ANY FRIENDS...

WHAT?

AND YUKI SEEMED VERY FOND OF HIM.

IT MAY HAVE BEEN INDISCREET, BUT I MUST ADMIT I WAS EXCITED TO WATCH HOW THEIR RELATIONSHIP WOULD DEVELOP IN THE FUTURE.

ALL THE WHILE, THE BOY SHE KNEW LOOKED AT THEM IN IRRITATION AND SOMETHING ELSE...

I NEVER IMAGINED SOMETHING SO TRAGIC WOULD HAPPEN YEARS LATER...

WHAT I
SAID TO YOU
THE OTHER
DAY STILL
STANDS.

DURING THE BATTLE AMONG PUREBLOODS, YUKI HAD LEFT TO RISK HER LIFE, AND SHE HAD RETURNED WITH A NEW LIFE INSIDE HER. THAT MOVED ME DEEPLY.

A PREGNANT VAMPIRE WILL BE OVERCOME BY THE THIRST OF TWO THROUGHOUT HER TERM. SHE CAN BE A THREAT TO THE PEOPLE AROUND HER.

RUKA, A FORMER STUDENT OF THE NIGHT CLASS, EXPLAINED EVERYTHING TO ME.

A VAMPIRE PREG-NANCY LASTS FROM TWO TO FIVE YEARS.

HMM...

AND...

...THAT'S MY STORY FROM THE TIME I MET YUKI...

...UNTIL SHE DISAPPEARED FOUR YEARS AGO.

I STILL REMEMBER THAT LOOK ON YOUR FACE AFTER SEEING YUKI SMILE FROM THE BOTTOM OF HER HEART...

IT'S BEEN HALF A CENTURY SINCE THAT DAY.

I REALLY THINK IT'S ABOUT TIME YOU TWO SETTLED DOWN.

UNLIKE HER...

...I HAVE ONE THING I REGRET.

...REGRET THAT I DIDN'T HONOR THAT MOMENT.
ALL I COULD THINK OF WAS LOSING YOU. I WANTED YOU WITH ALL MY HEART, BUT INSTEAD I TURNED MY BACK ON YOU...
ONE DAY, WHEN KANAME KURAN'S HEART IS RETURNED TO HIS BODY...
...I KNOW YOU'RE PLANNING TO GIVE YOUR OWN LIFE TO TURN HIM INTO A HUMAN.

I KNOW YOU ARE SIMPLY WAITING FOR THAT DAY TO COME...
...BUT UNTIL THEN, YOU ARE FREE TO DO ANYTHING YOU WANT WITH YOUR LIFE.
YOU SHOULD HONOR YOUR TIME TOO.

Golden Kamuy
Story and Art by Satoru Noda

In the early 20th century, Russo-Japanese War veteran Saichi "Immortal" Sugimoto scratches out a meager existence during the postwar gold rush on the wild frontier of Hokkaido. When he stumbles across a map to a fortune in hidden Ainu gold, he sets off on a treacherous quest to find it. But Sugimoto is not the only interested party, and everyone who knows about the gold will kill to possess it! Faced with the harsh conditions of the northern wilderness, ruthless criminals and rogue Japanese soldiers, Sugimoto will need all his skills and luck—and the help of an Ainu girl named Asirpa—to survive.

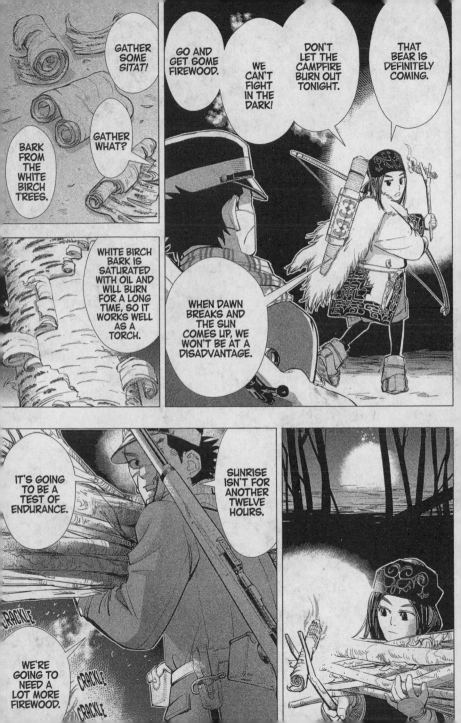

*THE AINU TERM FOR NON-AINU JAPANESE PEOPLE.

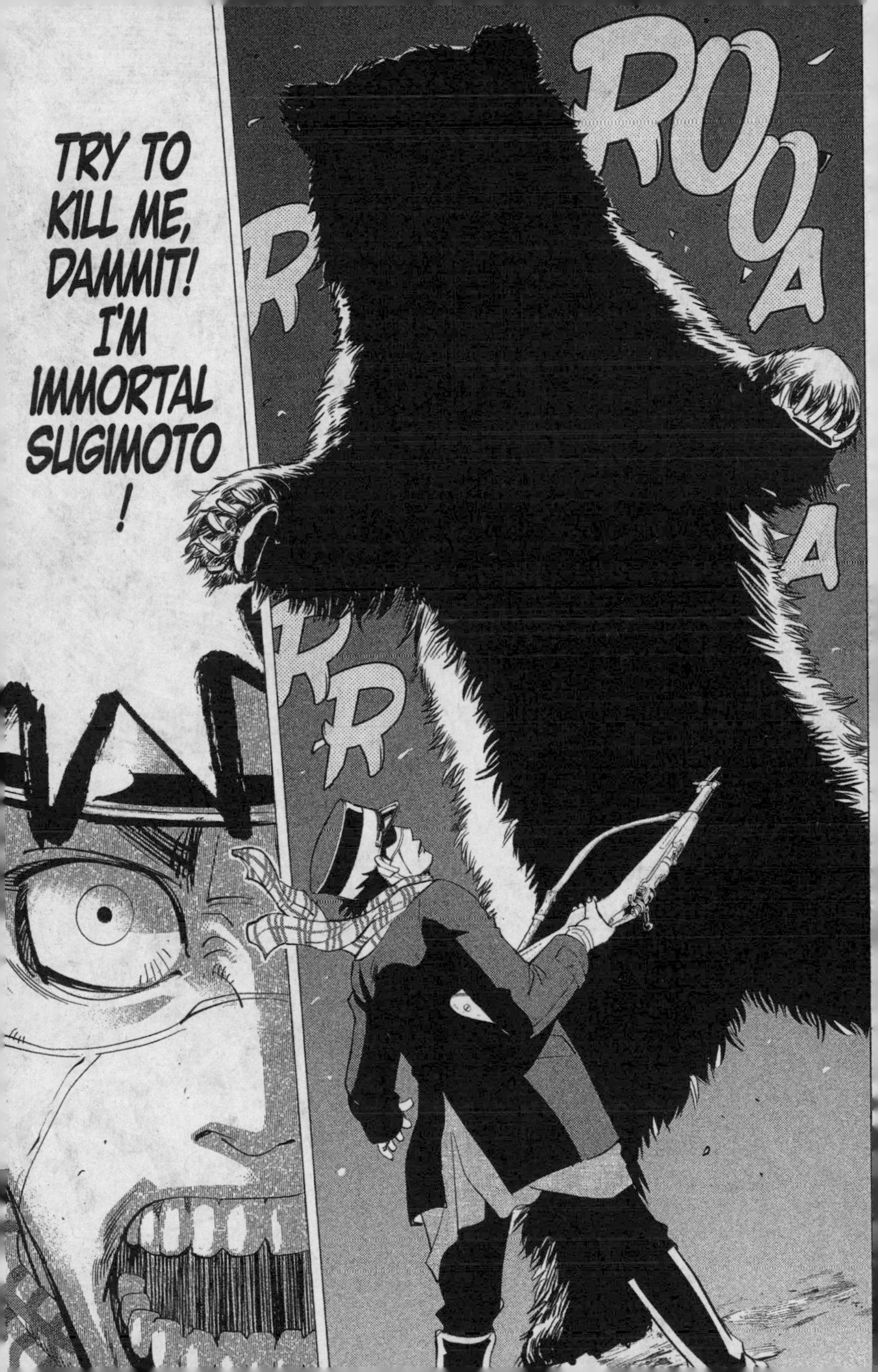
TRY TO KILL ME, DAMMIT! I'M IMMORTAL SUGIMOTO!
ROOOAAAA
RRRR

GRIP